TRINITY
COLLEGE LONDON PRESS

CW00408821

GRADE

04

PIANO

Pieces & Exercises for
Trinity College London
Exams 2018–2020

Includes CD &
teaching notes

Published by
Trinity College London Press
trinitycollege.com

Registered in England
Company no. 09726123

Printed in England by Halstan & Co Ltd., Amersham, Bucks

Minuet in E major

Johann Philipp Kirnberger
(1721-1783)

Play the repeats in the exam.

3

Allegretto

from *The London Sketchbook*, K. 15hh

Wolfgang Amadeus Mozart
(1756-1791)

Barcarolle
op. 100 no. 22

Friedrich Burgmüller
(1806-1874)

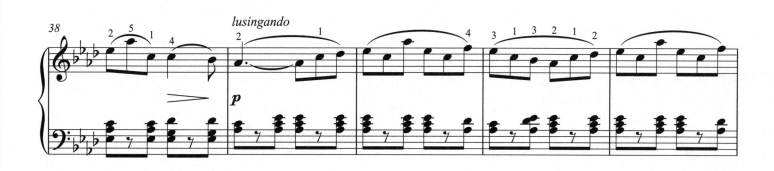

Andantino

First movement from *Sonatina*

Edward Elgar
(1857–1934)

Little Piece no. 17

from *20 Little Pieces for Beginners*, op. 6

Aleksandr Gedike
(1877-1957)

Por una Cabeza

Arr. Farrington

Carlos Gardel
(1890-1935)

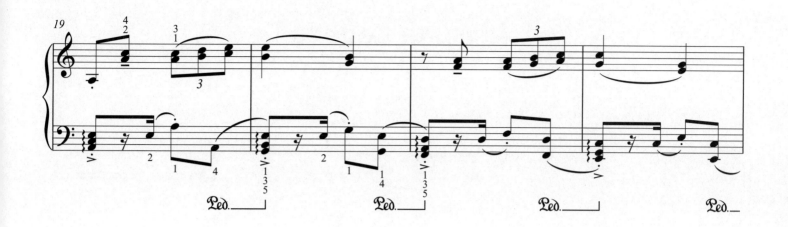

[Blank page to facilitate page turns]

Ballo Gaio

Henk Badings
(1907-1987)

Waltz Mystique

Ray Moore
(b. 1939)

The repeat must be played in the exam.

Tango Passionis

Barbara Arens
(b. 1960)

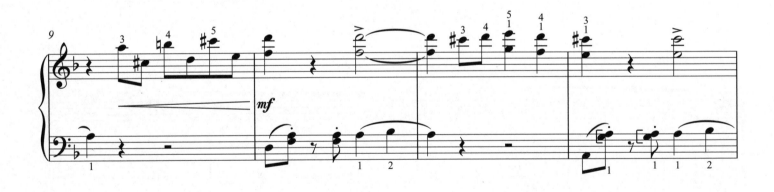

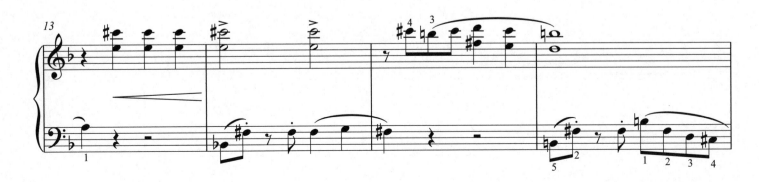

Exercises

1a. Little Waltz – tone, balance and voicing

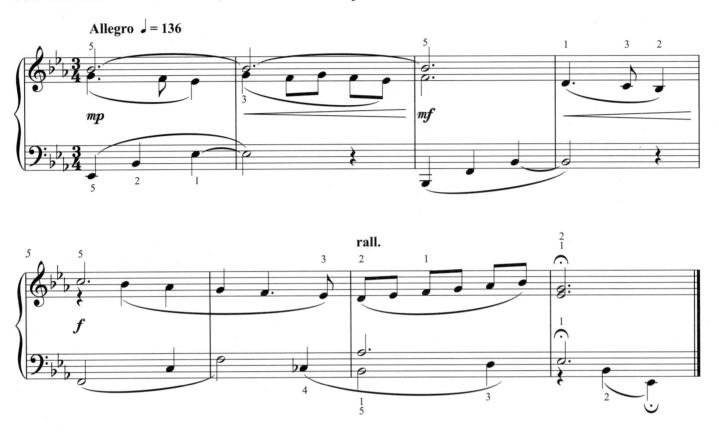

1b. Evening Sun – tone, balance and voicing

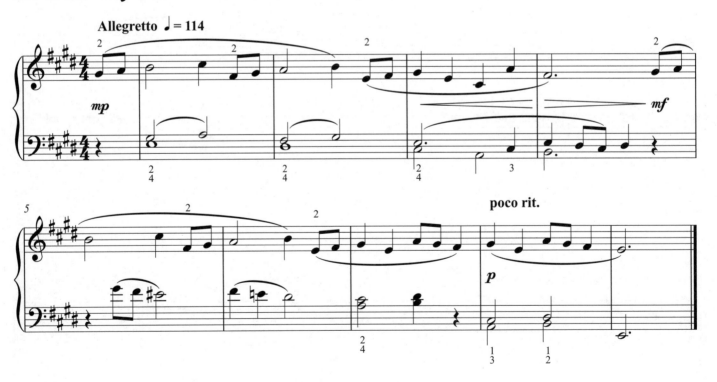

2a. Waltz Echoes – co-ordination

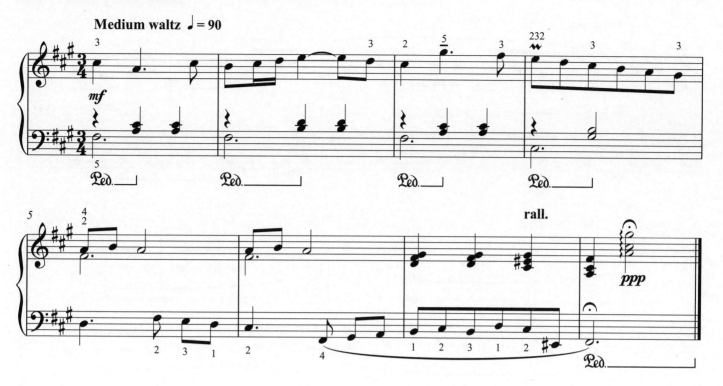

2b. A Walk in the Woods – co-ordination

3a. Timelines – finger & wrist strength and flexibility

3b. Roll up, roll up! – finger & wrist strength and flexibility

Teaching notes

Kirnberger   Minuet in E major   page 3

What an unusual term 'festivo' is, conjuring up thoughts of holidays and festivities, which suits the character of this cheerful minuet very well. The suggested tempo is challenging, given all the articulation detail to negotiate, but appropriate, and particularly necessary as repeats are requested for the exam. Kirnberger was one of J S Bach's students and a composer more known for his academic writing, both in musical style and in his theoretical studies, but there is little sign of that academicism here. Instead we have a celebration of E major and its related keys, with motifs formed from fragments of scales and broken chords.

A good starting point will be to visit these keys, practising scales and arpeggios in E, A and B majors. Try playing with different articulations too, perhaps four notes slurred at a time, or five slurred and one *staccato* (as in bar 5). We need to examine the score with a toothcomb: there are several quavers at the ends of bars that need separate articulation; many places where the hands play different articulations; and check the penultimate bar, as the pattern changes and is likely to catch pianists out. Crotchets that are unmarked are up to you – probably separated, but not as short as those with *staccato* dots. The energy and joy must not be lost in *p*; keep the fingers active. There's a saying for singers, sing softly but speak loudly, and you want something like that here – a stage whisper perhaps. With the many black notes in this key, there are moments of tricky fingering. What is suggested is generally good, but remember it is not illegal to use a thumb on a black note. For instance, I would play both the A and G♯ either side of the barline, bars 5-6, with a thumb, maintaining a good hand position for the ensuing quavers. Lastly Kirnberger has been fairly even-handed with his distribution of melodic material, so give the LH its fair share of the limelight.

Mozart   Allegretto (from *The London Sketchbook*, K. 15hh)   page 4

Wolfgang Amadeus wrote this when he was eight years old. He and his sister Nannerl were in London with their father and it is thought that the collection of pieces known as *The London Sketchbook* were composed while Leopold had a serious throat infection and the children were forbidden from playing the piano and disturbing their father. The pieces were written in pencil (very blunt and difficult to decipher in some cases) and contain the odd mistake or inconsistency. Here we see that the RH F in bar 16 is a dotted crotchet, merely a crotchet in bar 46, but a dotted crotchet again in bar 62. Should they really be different? I doubt very much that Mozart would have minded either way, but a little variety is seldom a bad thing.

The LH semiquavers in the D minor section will need careful practice to flow confidently. I'm not fond of using dotted rhythms as they tend to develop jerky movements, but you could instead try stopping every 4 notes, changing the note you start on, making sure those four notes are smooth and comfortable under the hand. I also like working backwards: play the last two semiquavers in bar 28, ending on the G in bar 29. Then add the previous two notes, then the whole of bar 28, then from the last two in bar 27, etc. You can also play it literally backwards, which really checks that you know the fingering and precisely where the hand has to be.

Bar 30 is a conundrum: was this a mistake of Mozart's, asking the RH to hold the D, whilst restriking it with the LH, or was he perhaps imagining an instrument with two keyboards? Either way, we need to find a solution and I suggest restriking it with the RH and then holding it as the LH plays the rest of the descending scale. Other solutions are possible!

No pedal is required; it wasn't in general use until much later than this. There are decisions to make about dynamic. For instance in bars 17-24 you will probably alternate between highlighting the RH for two bars, then the answering LH, and of course with so many repetitions of the main theme it would be entirely appropriate to vary the tone, perhaps finding a lighter colour for the reprise after the D minor section. The

unedited Urtext is a gift for experimenting with aspects of articulation and dynamic, matching both to mood and character, developing your imagination and technique along the way. Here decisions about articulation have been made for you, but it is good to know that they are editorial – the original pencil score has no such markings.

Mozart was of course a child prodigy and it is apt that this *London Sketchbook* found its way, probably through Mozart's wife, to another child prodigy, Felix Mendelssohn, whose family later gave it to a library in Berlin.

Burgmüller   Barcarolle, op. 100 no. 22   page 6

The gondola is tethered to a post, gently rocking in the water. First one, then another tourist steps in; the gondolier casts off, and serenades the couple as they sail down the Grand Canal in Venice.

Small adjusting wrist movements with fingers close to the keys will help to achieve the *legato* and *diminuendo* for the rocking gondola in the first two bars. Wait for the boat to steady itself after those first three chords – try to avoid counting the pause, instead listening to the sound and judging when is the precise right moment to re-start the *pianissimo* rocking. The second pause, moving to an unexpected C major, will be even longer, the *crescendo* more intense, with the LH *acciaccatura* adding impact to the climax without interfering rhythmically with the melodic progression from C to E♮ in the top voice. The chords will benefit from being pedalled, and some pedalling in the following *dolce* bars will help the couple get comfortable on their cushions. The serenade itself is probably accompanied by guitar or lute and if you do add some pedal to soften the edges of the chords, keep it discreet and be sure to separate them from each other, giving space in the texture for the serenade to project easily.

This barcarolle comes from a book of studies and it is the singing of the main melody that is being practised here, keeping the LH supportive, but in the background. Your fingering should be comfortable, allowing the weight of the arm to be carried from note to note. Check that wrists are flexible and above all listen to the sound, imagining it carrying gently over the water. A real *staccato* in bars 28 & 29 (does the boat bump the side of the canal here?), but keep the *sforzando* within the subdued dynamic. The penultimate *lusingando*, 'coaxing', phrase brings us back to the bank and as the gondolier ties his boat back to the post, perhaps he discovers, *perdendosi*, that the couple have fallen asleep. A beautifully structured piece, attractive, imaginative and pedagogically sound.

Elgar   Andantino (1st movt from *Sonatina*)   page 8

This is the first movement of a two-movement sonatina written for Elgar's niece. Tender, wistful, almost hesitant in places, yet also full of Elgarian warmth and generosity. There are several performances on YouTube, and the one by John Ogden is particularly beautiful, if a little slower than advised here.

It is difficult to *teach* the sense of style needed for such a piece – the *rubato*, the handling of the *largamentes*, allowing the music space to speak. I recommend listening to other works by Elgar, the *Enigma Variations*, the cello concerto, maybe the *Sea Pictures* or some of the symphonies. He has come to represent something quintessentially English, which is often linked to both reticence and nobility, but Elgar is also a masterly orchestrator. All of those elements are here: notice how the orchestration is different at the return of the theme in bar 25, with added *pizzicatos* and a sustained note in the horn; there is hesitation in the small phrases in bars 33-36, a gathering of confidence before the heartfelt *largamente* melody finally finds the courage to sing with certainty. Pedal throughout will add depth to the sound, being careful though not to sustain through rests, and both analyse and hear where the *appoggiaturas* occur and shape accordingly. Bar 6, bar 10, bar 12... listen for the difference in meaning between the two notes as tension turns into resolution, as the sound diminishes and the bar relaxes. The

LH fifth finger has an important role, sustaining some of the bass notes, playing them with slightly more weight than the other accompanying notes. The *acciaccatura* in bar 23 is short, but lyrical, heightening the expression in the *allargando*. No repeat in the exam.

Gedike — Little Piece no. 17 (from *20 Little Pieces for Beginners*) — page 10

Yes, Gedike is simply a variant spelling of Goedicke. Alexander Fyodorovich Goedicke was a Russian composer, first cousin to the more celebrated Nicolai Medtner. Examination boards keep Goedicke's name alive, but he is little heard in concert halls. Nevertheless pieces such as this are well-crafted and contain a wealth of musical detail in the service of a dramatic narrative, making them pedagogically useful as well.

The title is not helpful and I would encourage students to imagine their own storyline to match the colourful music. Someone runs on stage, stops, looks around searching for someone else...you get the picture! Articulation needs to match the character of the music: the *staccato* at the opening will be crisp, urgent, whereas in the *con anima* something less spiky will go better with the minor key and more pleading character. The upbeat to bar 32 should probably be the same as the other upbeats in this section, non-*legato*, making the reiteration of the F♯ in the LH possible, although a touch of pedal would not go amiss here. Small slurs abound and will need consideration. Some, as in bar 4, show the resolution of dissonances and need shaping with dynamics. Some build the tension, as in the opening gesture, or the scale in bars 15–16 (which should surely end in a climactic *staccato* in both hands). Others, as in the *Tranquillo*, seem to be marks of bowing, with slightly stronger down bows on the first note but with no major gap between up bow and down bow. Lastly, consider the silences as areas where things happen – tension dissipates or a new idea comes to the character – they should not feel empty. A good moment to talk about pregnant pauses perhaps? As Gedike instructs, be confident, be bold, and tell a story as you perform this.

Gardel arr. Farrington — Por una Cabeza — page 12

This is the first of two tangos in this selection, based on an original song for which Carlos Gardel wrote the music, Alfredo Le Pera the words. *Por una Cabeza* refers to a horse winning a race 'by a head' and the words talk of the singer's love for gambling and women...perhaps one not to research too closely! In both the sung versions and the arrangements for violin that abound on the internet there are many *portamenti* and many distortions of the rhythm. But for exam purposes keep the rhythms in the first section precise, not allowing the dotted rhythms to sag, but perhaps allow a little more leeway in the chorus, the A minor, with broad triplets more pleadingly lyrical above the tango bass.

Everyone has their own method for teaching two against three, as we have on the second page here. Nice cuppa tea is a firm favourite, and understanding the maths behind the combination, actually drawing the beat divided into the common denominator six, the second quaver fitting in between the second and third triplets, helps some learning styles enormously. Before playing the notes here, practise the rhythms on something much easier. Remember to use the arm to help with the thirds, a small impulse ensuring good synchronisation. Then add the foot into the mix...and of course, the character – this is quite rich and impassioned. A tricky few bars! In the first section use the wrist to help shape the RH phrases, small adjusting movements negotiating the black notes and ensuring that the fifth and sixth semiquavers taper effectively. There's a real tension between the upright exactness of the LH and the more shapely, weaving RH. In a way this represents an aspect of the dance, with the man generally leading, whilst his partner often has the more fancy footwork. Not an easy choice, but very satisfying when played well.

Badings — Ballo gaio — page 15

Coming in at around 30 seconds, this will give examiners little time to write, so be prepared to wait before your next piece! Dynamics are *f* or *p*, with one *crescendo*. During that *crescendo* the first notes of the bars are marked with accents, so listen for those increasing in volume as well. The *p* is both times accompanied by *leggiero*, so use a lighter touch, a gentler *staccato* than in the *f* sections, where the sound wants to be firm and direct. Imagine finger tips made of different materials – a crisp, starched linen for the *f* and a softer silk for the *p*. The *marcato* in bar 6 seems to relate to the LH, encouraging you to bring it more into focus for its solo motif, and notice that there is no *crescendo* at the end. Stay *piano*, if anything fading as you climb up the keyboard, with that very disconcerting overlapping of hands and phrases. The final chords, which are not marked *staccato*, are a final wink to the audience – despite the quasi-pompous opening, the whole thing has really been a piece of fun, a merry dance.

Henk, or Hendrik, Badings was a largely self-taught Dutch composer, who died relatively recently in 1987. Despite writing many large scale orchestral works, probably most of us have only come across his compositions on the exam syllabuses. A shame – there is wit and craft in this miniature.

Moore — Waltz Mystique — page 16

This mystical waltz has a fetching, rather forlorn theme that fits well under the fingers and should be quickly learnt. The harmonies are well chosen; the descending semitone bass is undoubtedly a cliché, but it nevertheless works well, and the foray into the Neapolitan major on the second page is particularly memorable. The challenge is in the variable articulation of the waltz accompaniment, changing from the first bar, whose slur throws the stress on to the second beat of the bar, to bar 5, where a sustained bass rings below detached second and third beat chords, to bar 10, which is neither one nor the other.

The central section moves into major territory and the dynamic comes up from the opening *p* to a more richly coloured *mf*. A good response to this change of mood would be to add in some pedalling, avoiding blurring the melody, but enabling the accompanying chords to sustain and add warmth and support. The rests in bar 27 signify a link back to the opening material, and this would be a good place to play *senza ped.* again as we approach the return of E minor. The *ritardando* in bar 30 will help ease back into the recapitulation. Experiment with playing the thirds in the first four bars divided between the hands and in bars 37–39 you could try playing thirds in the LH, leaving the RH able to project the top line more easily as you fade to *pp*. Do observe the short repeat in performance.

Arens — Tango Passionis — page 17

Barbara Arens has a piece in Grade 3 as well and once again it is possible to watch a YouTube clip of the composer herself performing this passionate tango. However, she does not stick exactly to the version published here, with some added sixths in places and some pedalling over rests. There is a long debate to be had over being meticulously faithful to the score or faithful to the spirit of score, and you could argue that listening to a composer's performance is evidence every bit as strong as the score itself. However, the score will be the primary source material for examiners and my advice would be to play what is written there rather than what you hear on YouTube.

Arens asks us to pedal with discretion. Use the pedal to enrich the sound, and to join what would otherwise be unjoinable, particularly the repeated sixths in bars 13, 17 & 19. Keep the integrity of the LH *staccato* as it occurs in bar 2; that is what gives this tango its straight-backed poise. As in Gardel's tango above, there is a subtle contrast between the more flexible, lyrical top part, and the firmness and rigour of the rhythmic interjections. Keep the LH close to the keys – jumping too high for the *staccatos* will make them sound looser, which is not what you are listening for here. More instruments seem to join in from bar 9; use the arm to find a full, deep sound on the sixths. The unusual *ritardando* then *accelerando* leads to a *forte* repeat of the opening. Take care not to shout here, easily done as you return to the middle of the keyboard. Instead make an effective *crescendo* and end with elan, *fortissimo*.

C P E Bach   Andante   *Faber*

This exquisite miniature by J S Bach's most well-known son is a real test of intimate, expressive playing and would have been well-suited to the gentler forebear of the piano, the clavichord. C P E Bach is associated with the *Empfindsamer Stil*, a style of writing that was more personal, more sensitive than that of the baroque period, and the poignant harmonies, wide-ranging, chromatic top line and the gentle comments from inner voices all add to the tender mood depicted here.

Many details to work on. Mordents should be on the beat in this period. One rule tells us that if a trill is preceded by the upper note, then it should begin on the note. But here I would suggest beginning both trills on the D. The previous D finishes a phrase and starting on the upper note adds dissonance and extra expressivity, as well as making the trill of demisemiquavers perfectly even. Bach asks for pedalling, but take care that this is used primarily to join the chords and not to blur the melody, which wants to be heard as from a solo instrument. Avoid holding the pedal for a whole minim, but rather listen to the integrity of the top line and change, or delay depressing, as necessary.

There are several places when the LH divides into two parts, bars 3-4, 5-7, etc. Practise these lines with two hands to hear the sustained notes and also to check which notes need to project more, to comment on or duet with the melody, then be sure to keep listening once you put it back together as written, checking that you can hear all three lines. Intervals do not all cost the same; a minor sixth should be more expensive, more expressive, than a major third. Hear the beauty of the diminished 7th in bar 9 and shape accordingly. The minor sixth in bar 15 seems a last reach towards an answer that never comes; give these special moments room to impact on a listener. Similarly the *tenuto* marks in bars 13 & 14 are to stress the chromaticism, just as you might lean on 'pain' when saying 'painful'. Not for everyone, but a joy for those awake to what it has to offer.

Bertini   Study in E minor   *Trinity*

This is a study in rhythmic evenness and finger control of fast triplet patterns, which both hands are required to execute with equal skill. The tempo is lively and the mood turbulent.

Make sure both hands sound precisely together at the beginning and end of the slurred triplet groups (ie bars 1-2), and taper the phrase off so we hear a very clear *diminuendo*. Crotchets not under a phrase mark should be detached (assume a *staccato* touch). The slurs in bars 8 and 16 apply to the triplets only; the crotchet above will be short. Pay careful attention to the part writing in the RH in bars 11-12; insist that long notes are held and shorter notes released. Avoid a *crescendo* through bar 14 – the $f\!f$ at bar 15 needs to be sudden and dramatic.

Grieg   Walt in A minor   *Schott*

Edvard Grieg composed groups of *Lyric Pieces* throughout his life, the first when he was in his twenties and the last set six years before his death. The beautiful Arietta, the very first one, has been a Grade 5 piece and is now in Trinity's *Raise the Bar* volume. Grieg memorably revisited the same melody in his very last lyric piece, Remembrances, thereby coming full circle, reworking the material in the light of a further 34 years' experience. This Waltz is the second in the first set, directly following the Arietta, sharing some of its quiet melancholy.

Grieg directs performers to use the pedal but, whereas the first section has a plethora of *staccato* dots, the slurs in the central A major section suggest a more lyrical, *legato* approach. Even the accompanying chords here are marked *portamento*. So my advice would be to use the pedal on the first beat only for most of the A minor section, but to use it far more generously in the A major. There is a problem with the contrasts between *staccato* and *legato* in the two hands on some downbeats, for instance bar 5. My solution is to play the top note of the first chord with the RH, allowing the LH to make the *legato* between bass and chord without the pedal. Easy once you get used to it. The A major part also has its challenges. Some nifty fingerwork is needed in bar 39, the RH releasing the C♯ so that the LH can play it, and then vice versa – another reason for the pedal being essential here. The *acciaccatura* is

also surprisingly tricky: it should come before the beat in this romantic style, so you are effectively repeating the G♯, but making it softer the second time so that the stress is on the downbeat dissonance, the F♯. You may like to try swapping the hands for this section – it works surprisingly well! Keep the f in proportion to the overall mood, and maybe use *una corda* for the final *pianissimo* bars. Much repetition here, so it is nowhere near as long as it looks, and a tempo of around ♩ = 138, with a definite sense of one-in-a-bar works well.

Kirchner   Dreaming Lake   *Breitkopf*

What an unusual piece. Over before you know it and packed with detail. Discreet pedalling enhances the sound world; you will probably want to change with most quavers, adding a slight aura of mistiness around the edges of this lake. A tempo of ♩ = 58 is good, but keep this flexible – there is no metronome ticking as your raft floats on this dreaming lake.

Theodor Kirchner led a chequered life, but was well-respected by his fellow German romantic composers, such as the Schumanns and Mendelssohn. He wrote many such miniatures, some of which find their way on to examination syllabuses, but they are often, as here, musically sophisticated and need sensitivity and subtlety in performance. The slurs in *Dreaming Lake* should be seen as phrase marks – a gap in the sound is not appropriate. The handovers, as one instrument after another plays the rocking motif, should be unhurried and respond to the harmonies. The second voice takes us up to D minor – heightened expressivity here – then the next two voices bring us back to A minor and down an octave, so shape those accordingly. Even where no dynamics are marked this piece is continually in flux, moving up and down on gentle ripples of sound. Careful voicing needed in the next exchange as a smaller motif works its way down to the middle voice in bars 7-8, making a *ritardando* en route, and with a sustained bass line bringing things to a half close. The *crescendo* in bar 14 needs to be enough to take the tension through the rests, but not to be too shrill on the top octaves. The *staccato* should also fit the story, separated, yes, but not too short to disturb the sleepy atmosphere. By giving us a descriptive title Kirchner has given us licence to build our own narrative – what's your story?

Maxwell Davies   Calm Water (from *Stevie's Ferry to Hoy*)   *Boosey*

This is a piece to meditate by; you can't play it well if half your mind is thinking about something else. It demands complete focus, a sense of being in the zone, of switching off from the world's hassles and losing yourself in the moment, in the peace of this music. Three minutes of mindfulness! So much of Peter Maxwell Davies' music was inspired by the special atmosphere of the Orkney Islands; he is already much missed.

As the ferry takes you back to the Orkneys the waves gently overlap each other, the RH needing to hear two individual voices rather than chords. When the melody enters in the bass the sound can be a little fuller. Notice how the phrases again overlap, with a singing five bars in the cello, playing with a different moment in the top parts' cycle as it repeats – listen to be sure your phrasing captures this subtlety. The pedal can be used discreetly throughout the piece, but time seems to stop with the B♭ – so far we've heard only white notes – and the pedal here is held over 7 bars. I hear the B♭s as bells, a warning that the ferry is approaching land through the mist. Give them extra depth and ringing projection. This music is reworked on its return, and notice the long pedal from bar 47 to the end. The hands are crossed here, but then uncross as the RH plays above the LH, the last line marked two octaves higher, and barely audible. Check posture when the LH crosses over – no need to raise the shoulder! *Calm Water* needs a calm pianist with care for sound and mood. Around ♩ = 108.

| Mozart | Menuetto and Trio (from *Viennese Sonatina no. 6*) | Universal |

This is a challenging choice for Grade 4, with a lot of material to learn, alongside copious musical detail. It also requires a sophisticated understanding of this refined Mozartian style, and it's long, so no repeats in the exam and be ready for the examiner to stop you before the DC. In my edition the metronome mark is 72 to a bar, but this is too ambitious, and a crotchet pulse of 132 is more realistic for this level, keeping more or less the same tempo for the trio. An important consideration is that these are arrangements, not original Mozart. He wrote them as wind divertimentos in 1783 and we are not sure who arranged them – probably Ferdinand Kauer, but definitely not Mozart. There are places where the articulation is awkward and counter-intuitive, for instance in bars 3 and 41-42. It is based on the wind parts, where individual instruments can more easily play contrasting articulation, but definitely in bars 41-42 I would suggest you separate the LH sixths to match the RH.

Do listen to the original version, K439b. The emphasis is on gracefulness, precision, elegant shaping of all the phrases, and an avoidance of any harshness in the *forte* playing. Listen for the shaping of 6/4 to 5/3 progressions as in bar 4 – such a staple element of this style. The dynamic contrasts in the trio should be achieved through increased use of arm weight, but always keeping the wrist supple, able to transfer the weight into the keys without unnecessary tension. There is a fun bassoon solo in bars 37-40 in the trio, so allow this bass line to project while the oboe weaves a quaver line above it. I doubt whether anyone would have danced to this divertimento, but there is still that buoyancy in the pulse, a poise in the rhythms that you can often find by imagining conducting a group, the physical gestures, and the looking towards different instrumentalists helping you to inhabit the pulse. Ultimately the whole piece needs to sound effortless – the most difficult challenge of all. But I do hope that some pianists will be courageous enough to take it on...

| Neefe | Arioso | Bärenreiter |

This rather lovely Arioso also sounds like an arrangement, perhaps from a string trio this time. Christian Gottlob Neefe was a contemporary of Mozart's and was primarily known for his operas. But he was also one of Beethoven's early teachers and there is something about the richness of the writing that reminds me of the sort of theme Beethoven may write and then use as the basis of variations. As the title suggests, this is mainly a solo aria for the first violin, with occasional interpolations from the other players, and demands a singing tone, careful balancing of all three voices, and good foot control.

The opening cello gesture is noteworthy and needs shaping, a *diminuendo* as you relax down the octave. The majority of the footwork is *legato* pedalling but you could use direct pedalling for bar 17, for variety and to respect the *portamento* articulation. Direct pedalling means that the pedal is released and depressed as you release and depress the notes, rather than the opposite, giving you a small space between the chords. There are other places with similar markings in the RH, but with *legato* in the LH and I feel it sounds pedantic to highlight the difference in this context, so would use the *portamento* indication as a reason to lift the RH, ensuring good synchronisation of the sixth, while maintaining *legato* pedalling. Listen carefully in bar 19 – you may want to delay depressing the pedal so as not to blur the syncopated violins. The middle section features more of a duet between the top two voices. Keep the dotted rhythms poised and precise and consider playing the second violin with the LH in bar 14. You could slightly ease the tempo into the recapitulation. Throughout feel those top fingers tingling with the special vibrato that the solo violin will use to project this simple but noble theme. The thumb should feel looser, holding on to its longer notes, but allowing the first violin's line to be bathed in a warm, mellow spotlight.

| Petot | You Have to Shake It | Kjos |

I'm sure that this will appeal to many although put beside the Mozart, Neefe, Maxwell Davies, etc, there is relatively little musical interpretation required! Nevertheless, there is a time-honoured tradition of having a blues in the Grade 4 syllabus and Petot has given us a particularly energetic example. Originally the blues grew from an oral tradition, with a vocal line improvised over the primary triads, with the 12-bar blues developing into a sequence of I, I, I, I, IV, IV, I, I, IV, V, I, I. The mood was, as the name suggests, usually melancholy. Petot has taken the harmonic structure, but made the mood more upbeat, eschewed melodic content, given 'funky' as a direction, and written a particularly creative coda.

Start by improvising your own blues to become fully comfortable with the chord structure. Try using Petot's substitute for the subdominant in bar 9 – a wonderful supertonic with both major and minor thirds. This F♯ is part of the blues scale on C, as are the B♭s and E♭s, so work those into your improvised melodies. The actual notes of this piece should then be quickly learnt. Notice the *loco* in bar 25 and don't automatically make a *diminuendo* with the *ritardando* at the end – it's not marked and it fits the mood more to stay *forte*. Try not to be too pedantic about the triplets – they need to sound easy and insouciant. The repeated chords in bar 12 need to lead back to the opening, so begin them a little softer so that you can *crescendo* into the next downbeat. Make sure your arm is behind all the thirds, staying close to the keys and with little fingers well supported from the bridge. Examiners will be well aware that this is an easy choice, so listen out for every detail, keeping that high-octane energy, albeit controlled from a cool head, from the first to the last note.

| Sutermeister | Erster Ferienmorgen | Schott |

The first morning of the holidays – definitely a cause for celebration, which is just the mood Sutermeister has captured in this piece. As so often with two-page pieces, there is quite a bit of repetition and most of the semiquaver work is scalic, so should lie quite comfortably under the fingers. It would be worth revising B♭ major before starting.

The *staccatos* want to be quite chirpy, with extra energy in those marked with an accent. Watch out for the odd chord marked with a line instead of a dot; these want to be held for their full length. Neat part-playing needed in bars 7-8, checking that there is a four-note D major chord sounding on the last beat. For the central section the hands swap roles, the theme passing into the LH. One of the most difficult things to do is to play such five-finger patterns well, particularly when the *crescendo* is towards the fifth finger. Although the most obvious fingering is to use 1, 2, 3, 4, 5 on consecutive notes, if this is not working well then 1, 2, 3, 1, 2 is a possible alternative – or even 1, 2, 3, 1, 4. The contrasting dynamics will help bring the last lines to life. The **pp** marking does not just mean very soft, but is also full of anticipation; the **ff** is exultant, not hard. Notice the change from G to G♭ in RH, bars 19-20 – easily missed! A fairly straightforward piece, painted in clear, bright colours. Performers need to be able to project this sense of excitement, without getting too excited themselves.

| Terzibaschitsch | The Old Gramophone | Trinity |

Vinyl is making a comeback, so maybe younger pianists will have experience of the needle getting stuck. If not, the joke behind this will take some explaining but it is cleverly done.

The needle gets stuck three times. When it does in real life there is an ugly sound as it catches, then it takes a second to re-find the groove. Terzibaschitsch has written a *sf* on what is clearly in context a wrong chord, and lets us choose how many times the needle catches before it sets itself to rights. I suggest that you slightly fall forward (rhythmically!) into the *sf* then take a fraction longer than usual to find the next note. To anyone who has experienced it, this slight distortion of the rhythm comes naturally but for the young and innocent there is no doubt somewhere online where you can hear this happening! Try not to have the same number of repeats each time – it's probably better to decide how many to do, but some of you may wish to be inspired in the moment.

Apart from this imaginative trick, the rest of the piece is also delightful, with a typical, detached waltz accompaniment and a lilting melody. It is the very contrast of the elegance of the music and the ugly distortions that make this such fun, so employ your most graceful phrasing elsewhere, and check that you don't physically tense when the needle is sticking. 56 bars a minute, and as fast as you can safely manage the coda.

Trad. *arr.* Holt   Bop Goes the Weasel   *Spartan*

A clever play on words for this entertaining and ultimately fairly straightforward piece. All the directions you need are written into the music and the suggested tempo is excellent. Dotted rhythms to be swung, played as easy-going triplets, and that includes places, like bars 4 or 26, where you have a combination of dotted crotchet and quaver. *Acciaccaturas* should be played crushed just before the beat. Note that where there is no slur notes should be articulated, so *legato* for the first half of bar 8, then non-*legato* thereafter. Bars 13–15 are the most devious: first you have a quick change from *legato* to non-*legato* in the RH, working against the longer LH chords, then the RH has *staccato* crotchets against those marked *tenuto* in the LH. Well, this is Grade 4, so there need to be some challenging moments! It goes without saying that if you cannot stretch the octave, and easily play the *acciaccatura* in the final bar, then this one isn't for you. The mood is jaunty, swaggering, hands in pockets, so make a full sound for the f passages – hear those trombones joining in – but keep the smile in the sound.

Teaching notes written by Pamela Lidiard

Key

A solid line denotes a piece within this book.

A dotted line denotes a piece from the alternative list.